P9-DDD-122

Sneeze-activated flash!

Luxurious fur!

Zoom lens!

THIS BOOK IS BROUGHT TO YOU BY

NOSEPIX 500

THE WORLD'S FIRST 10-MEGAPIXEL MUSTACHE!

For quality pics, all you need is your nose and your finger!

Snap secret photos of your buddies!

Take candid shots of your oatmeal!

Download straight from your nostril to your computer!

And print out your precious moments with the . . .

INK BEARD PRINTER ATTACHMENT

Sold Separately and Expensively

FROM

SWISS

UPPER LIP

YOUR MUSTACHE AUTHORITY

KIRK SCROGGS

SNOOP TROOP

ATTACK OF THE NINJA POTATO CLONES

SCHOLASTIC INC.

This book is a work of fiction. Names, characters, places, and incidents are the product of the author's imagination or are used fictitiously. Any resemblance to actual events, locales, or persons, living or dead, is coincidental.

No part of this publication may be reproduced, stored in a retrieval system, or transmitted in any form or by any means, electronic, mechanical, photocopying, recording, or otherwise, without written permission of the publisher. For information regarding permission, write to Little, Brown Books for Young Readers, a division of Hachette Book Group, Inc., 1290 Avenue of the Americas, New York, NY 10104.

ISBN 978-0-545-93920-1

Copyright © 2015 by Kirk Scroggs. All rights reserved.
Published by Scholastic Inc., 557 Broadway, New York, NY 10012, by arrangement with Little, Brown Books for Young Readers, a division of Hachette Book Group, Inc.
SCHOLASTIC and associated logos are trademarks and/or registered trademarks of Scholastic Inc.

12 11 10 9 8 7 6 5 4 3 2 1 15 16 17 18 19 20/0

Printed in the U.S.A. 40

First Scholastic printing, November 2015

Special thanks to Steve Deline; Joanna Stampfel-Volpe; Jaida Temperly; Danielle Barthel; Hiland Hall; Mark Mayes; Joe Kocian; Mamacita; Corey; Candace; Charlotte; and Isaac; and a mega macho mustachioed thanks to Andrea Spooner, Deirdre Jones, Tracy Shaw, Russell Busse, and the rest of the Little, Brown Troopers!

An Important Message from the Narrator

Hey, amateur private eyes!

Some spud brain is stealing all of Murkee City's potato supply. French fries, Tater Tots, yams, you name it! Pretty soon we'll all be eating crayons and glue if this keeps up! See if you can help the Snoop Troop crack the case by paying close attention, especially anytime you see a magnifying glass like the one right here. Now, if I can only find my car keys, I can get out of this creepy alley! This narrating is dangerous work!

MISSING!
GERTIE
THIS SIGN FOR SALE!
Find Gertie!

CHAPTER 1

HOT POTATO

A lazy, peaceful afternoon on Baskerville Lane . . .

Birds are chirping. . . .

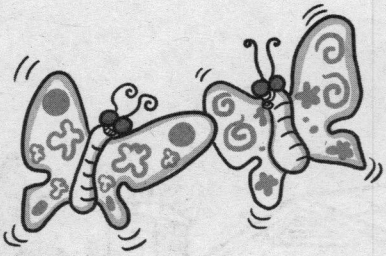

Butterflies are fluttering. . . .

Old Man Jorgensen is watering his petunias. . . .

Old Man Jorgensen's dog is watering Old Man Jorgensen. . . .

All is tranquil with the world.

Until the silence is broken by wild, piercing shrieks coming from an abandoned ice-cream truck!

Is it an elderly woman being kidnapped? A baby screaming for its pacifier? A cat with its tail caught in an electric egg beater?

Ah yes, I forgot. It's fifth-grade powerhouse private eyes Logan Lang and Gustavo Muchomacho. Ever since they started the Snoop Troop Detective Agency in Logan's mom's old ice-cream truck, they've been sharing trade secrets with each other.

That's right. Every time we meet, I educate Gustavo in the art of old-school detective work—classic Scotland Yard sleuthing, yo!
Putting "yo" at the end of that sentence doesn't make it cool, yo.
DAME EDITH MYSTERIES
AFTER-DINNER MYSTERIES
FIBER SAMPLES
FORENSICS
MYSTERY
DEDUCING JUSTICE
When she's done with the boring stuff, I show her how a real cop gets it done. We're talkin' bustin' perps, gettin' bad guys, and knockin' heads!
Don't worry. Only a mannequin.
WHAPO!

Well, at least it looks like you two have become best friends.

Good buddies?

Two humans who barely tolerate each other?

All of a sudden, a million emergency vehicles zoom by with sirens wailing!

WALL OF MUSTACHES
COP
JALAPEÑO SUNDAE
TARGET
P. J. PANTZ is...
LOADED
POP!
FRUIT!
SLURP!
Now, where is that TV remote? Sherlock Holmes would be ashamed if he saw such a pigsty of an office.
I won't tell him if you won't.
ONE ANGRY COP
Video games
HERO
COMICS
WHEELIE
CHEEZ KRINKLES
BULK CHEEZ KRINKLES
EVIDENCE
ACTION MUSTACHE!
FIRES MISSILES!
DWARF MISSILE BLASTER

Find the TV remote!
THE 5TH ANNUAL SLEUTH AWARDS
FUDGE BAR
LOGAN
MAP
WOLF BANE
THE SHAPE-SHIFTER SAGA
THE HEART THROBS LOUDEST JUST BEFORE DAWN...
SHERLOCK AWARD
CASE FILE #1
MOLES
YOUNG FORENSICS SET
FILE #3
MISSING IN ACTION
THE BUTLER DID IT
CRIME
SLEUTH TROOP
CRIME SCENE BUSTERS
DVD
FABRIC SAMPLE
KID CLUES
FINGERPRINT DETECTIVE
INCLUDES INK AND FINGERS
FIBER SAMPLES
WHO WHAT WHY
CLUE
BULK MAGNIFY GLASSES
CHOCO BAR
MURKEE CITY
FILE

I found the remote! It's in Wheelie's mouth. Better get it out before he . . .
GULP!
. . . swallows it.
Urp!

Wheelie is Logan's cranky old dog. Ever since he was a puppy, he's been known to eat a variety of things he isn't supposed to . . .

Like Logan's mom's wedding cake . . .

Uncle Fred's wooden leg . . .

And let's not forget the Cinco de Mayo Jalapeño Incident of 2012.

Luckily, this isn't the first time Wheelie has snarfed the remote, and Logan knows just what to do.

NEWS FLASH!
ALMOST FRESH
This just in—cops are rushing to the Almost Fresh Grocery Store, where a robbery is going down in the produce department!
No word on injuries yet, but witnesses did spot several bruised bananas and six beaten eggs!
Grab your magnifying glass and put on your snooping shoes, rookie. We're heading to the grocery store!
Great timing! I happen to be running low on Nuclear Cinnamon Balls and athlete's foot powder.

ALMOST FRESH
GROCERIES
EXIT
SALE 2 FOR 1!
SPECIAL! 1 FOR 2!
OPEN
SALE! BUTTERMILK $2.99
Po-Po
Po-Po

CHAPTER 2

AISLE OF TERROR

The Almost Fresh Grocery Store. When Logan and Gustavo arrive, the joint is crawling with cops and killer bargains. I mean, just look at that sale sign. Organic buttermilk for $2.99 a carton? They charge twice that over at Partial Foods on Main Stree—

Sorry, I got carried away. Just how do you expect to sneak past the police anyway?

Uh-oh.

It looks like Gustavo has slipped into the store unnoticed. That's Captain Mosely of the Murkee City Police Department and his deputies surveying the crime scene. The joint is a topsy-turvy wreck.

Logan sneaks in like a stealthy panther and joins Gustavo in a barrel of roasted peanuts. She's a little upset with him for sneaking off. He is technically still in training.

You could've blown our cover sneaking in here like that! I oughtta revoke your magnifying glass. . . .
ROASTED GOOBERS
CAUTION: MAY CONTAIN NUTS.
Holy cow! Look at the size of that yam!
ROASTED GOOBERS
CAUTION: MAY CONTAIN NUTS.
That's not a yam. It's my nose. . . .
ROASTED GOOBERS
CAUTION: MAY CONTAIN NUTS.
I have a mild nut allergy.
ROASTED GOOBERS
CAUTION: MAY CONTAIN NUTS.

Look! Captain Mosely's interviewing Mr. Mister, the grocer. We need to move in closer so we can hear what they're saying.
I've got just the thing!

My spritzing Old Man Mustache. With this gray facial fur, this apron, and my swollen nose, we can slip right past the po-po.

NEW FROM
SWISS
UPPER LIP
YOUR MUSTACHE AUTHORITY
OLD MAN MUSTACHE
WITH SPRITZING ACTION!
FEATURES TWO 10-OZ SPRAY NOZZLES.
ORDER NOW
AND GET A FREE OLD MAN HANDKERCHIEF!
HONK!
KEEPS UPPER LIP HYDRATED AND SHINY.
HANDY FOR GARDENING.
SPRAY BUTTER ON FOOD WITH EASE!
POP CORN
ARTIFICIAL BUTTER CARTRIDGE SOLD SEPARATELY
BUTTER FLAVOR
BUTTER FLAVOR

Moments later, a kindly old grocer steps onto the scene spritzing the produce.

Just keep spritzing, Gustavo. I'm moving in closer so I can do a police sketch of the culprit.
Okay, Mr. Mister, give me a detailed description of the robber, and make it quick. I have to get home and watch *The Real Nannies of Atlanta*.
LETTUCE
H_2O

Pay attention to Mr. Mister's description and draw the suspect on a piece of scratch paper, the chalkboard, or your best friend's forehead while he's napping!

He was about three feet tall and was wearing a tight black bodysuit. He had a hood over his big round head and only his bulgy eyes and little nose were peeking out. He was barefoot and jumping around like a gymnast.
SALAD FIXIN'S
DRESSING ROOM
RANCH
CABBAGE
IT'S WHUT'S FOR DINNER.

Whoa! I think the suspect might be a tiny ninja.
Hiii . . . YA!
Hmmm . . . That's the fifth local potato robbery this week. Soon there won't be enough spuds for French fries, mashed potatoes, or Tater Tots.
What's really weird is, he only took the potatoes.
TOES
POTATOES

No Tater Tots?!
NOOOOOO!!!
Excuse me. Did your belly just cry out for Tater Tots?
Must've been the lunch I ate. You'd be amazed at what my belly can do after a seven-layer burrito.

Captain Mosely sees right through their disguise and rips off the grocer's apron.

All right, men! According to this map of the store, there is one rear exit we need to cover.
REAR

Uh, sir... that's a deli chart of choice pork cuts.
DELI MEAT
BACK FAT
REAR
BACON
PORK SHOULDER
PORK BELLY
Mmm... bacon.

While Captain Moseley is yelling . . . er, giving his skilled team of experts a pep talk, Logan and Gustavo set out to search for more evidence.

Au contraire! If you hadn't been napping when I showed you episode ten of the *Dame Edith Mysteries*...
DECAF
ALL CAF
COFFEE PLOT
CUP OF JOE COFFEE
CUP OF JOE COFFEE
CUP OF JOE COFFEE FRESH GROUND
CAFE
...you would have noticed she used dried coffee grounds to reveal wet footprints in the rose garden.
CUP OF JOE COFFEE
The grounds clump up on anything wet.
CLUB SODA
Now we just follow the trail of prints!
Wow! The janitor is going to hate your guts!

The footprints lead to the aisle of frozen foods, a cold and lonely place.

Logan senses someone lurking amid the TV dinners and frozen lima beans.

Suddenly, a bite-sized ninja bursts out of the pizza section and hurls a frozen Sausage and Mushroom Supreme!

The whirling disc of death with extra garlic smacks Logan in the noggin!

The peewee punk pounces into the Meat Department and leaps up onto a table . . . then makes his escape through an air vent in the ceiling!

Hello! I think he knicked himself and left something behind!
Gnarly!
It's shaped like a human toe, but there's no blood. It's pure white and crisp like a . . . like a potato!

Mr. Mister, an amateur potato expert, confirms Logan's theory. It is indeed a toe-shaped potato–or a pota*toe*, one might say. Logan and Gustavo share their discovery with Captain Mosely.

The cap'n sure has a weird way of saying thanks!
WHUMP!
Partner, we must commit all our resources and manpower to protecting our city's precious Tater Tots!

In case you hadn't noticed, Logan really likes Tater Tots.

NEWS
2% MILK
HAVE YOU SEEN THIS SPUD?
This just in! Police are baffled by a mysterious rash of potato thefts! In other news, I'm baffled by a mysterious rash on my left elbow!
MURKEE MORNING MOJO
MYSTERY POTA-TOE FOUND AT SCENE
Ketchup
DR. SNOTE
PEDIATRICIAN SAYS, "IT LOOKS LIKE A TOE, TASTES LIKE A FRENCH FRY."

Google News
POTATO THEFTS CONTINUE!
SEVERED TOE LEAVES COPS STUMPED
CLICK HERE FOR FULL STORY
YESTERDAY'S NEWS
50¢
COPS CALL POTATO THEFT HALF-BAKED
CAPTAIN MOSELY- HEAD OF POLICE
NINJA MAY BE RESPONSIBLE
MR. MISTER- HEAD OF LETTUCE
THE ELABORATOR
STOCKPILES OF POTATOES DEPLETED!
TATERS
STOCKPILES OF SOUR CREAM AND CHIVES OVERFLOWING
DOG BARKS "LA VIDA LOCA" IN CHARMING SKIRT

Notice anything weird?
GO Marlins!

CHAPTER 3

THE MURKEE TALENT POOL

Murkee Elementary School. It's the next morning, and the hallways are abuzz with gossip about the Great Potato Robbery. Principal Shrub tries to ease everyone's minds about the tater shortage.

To make matters even tenser, it's the day of the big Mini Murkee Talent Show. After lunch the kindergartners are set to wow the entire student body with an explosion of raw talent and cuteness.

Never resting for a second, Logan brings her notes and sketches on the potato theft to the auditorium. She is joined by an unexpected guest.

I'm afraid you two will have to work on the case later. Principal Shrub is here to get the show started.

Something about that pale blond munchkin looks awfully familiar.

Uh-oh.

IIIIIII'm a
Yankee Doodle
Daaaaaaaan-deeeeee. . . .
I ♥ CHEESE
INCOMING!
I ♥ CHEESE

WHOMP!
Parents! Students! You can stop screaming. The threat has been forcefully tackled!
This is not what I meant by "a warm Murkee welcome"!

Moments later, the Snoop Troop find themselves waiting outside Principal Shrub's office.

Shrub calls them in for a stern talking-to.

Gustavo is terribly sorry he tackled you in front of your peers and parents. Shake hands?
'Twas nothing. Forgive my clammy hands. I have over-active sweat glands.
I ♥ CHEESE
How can you just let him get away? He's the potato ninja!
Highly unlikely.
I ♥ CHEES
His feet have the normal amount of toes on each foot.

Principal Shrub lets them off with just five detentions, with time off for good behavior.

WALL OF MUSTACHES
COP
DETECTIVE P. J. PANTZ IS...
ONE ANGRY COP
Gustavo's sad puppy-dog face
GUSTAVO
DEEP FREEZE
COP
COMICS
PIZZA
ACTION!
POLICE!
CASE FILE
ACTION
Wheelie's sad puppy-dog face
THE MISSING LINK
GET A CLUE
MYSTERY MEAT

CHAPTER 4

A SECOND HELPING

After school, Logan feels pretty rotten watching Gustavo clean out his desk. It doesn't help that he's making his sad puppy-dog face.

Suddenly, there's a breaking news flash on the TV!

Actual surveillance photo from Suds & Spuds!
BAKED POTATO
PLAIN SPUD... $2.99
ADD ONS
CHEESE ... $.99
CHILI ... $.99
CHIVES ... $.99
HOT FUDGE ... $.99
DRY CLEANING
PANTS ... $5.99
DRESS SHIRT... $3.99
SUIT ... $20.00
SUPER HERO CAPE... $10.00
WE PRESS PANTS AND PANINIS.
CASH ONLY
SODA
$2.99
MACARONI CHEESE
LAUNDRY
PANTS
POTATO BAR
SUDS
Look closely!
CLUE
SUPPORTING PUBLIC TELEVISION
MYSTERY

Look, there in the mirror! That's Chapster! I told you he's the potato thief!
But it doesn't add up. This robbery happened at three o'clock, while Chapster was in Principal Shrub's office with us!
BAKED POTATO
PLAIN SPUD...$2.99
ADD ONS
CHEESE ... $.99
CHILI ... $.99
CHIVES ... $.99
HOT FUDGE ... $.99
DRY CLEANING
PANTS ... $5.99
DRESS SHIRT... $3.99
SUIT ... $20.00
SUPER HERO CAPE... $10.00
WE PRESS PANTS AND PANINIS.
SODA
LAUNDRY
PANTS
SUDS
POTATO BAR
SUPPORTING PUBLIC TELEVISION
MYSTERY

Suddenly there's a knock at the door!

Logan slowly opens the door to find . . .

AAAAHH!
Greetings, Snoop Troopsters. I bring an offering of homemade Gouda cheese.
WITCH-SICKLE
BUBBLE GUM WART
KOALA
WITH BUBBLE GUM NOSE
CHEESE
SCREAM!
11 SCOOP CONE
FILE
LIL' CRIMINALS
FILE

It's Chapster!
Gee, uh, thanks. Why are you here exactly?
Just to say there are no hard feelings and that my pediatrician, Dr. Snote, said I have no broken bones from being so brutally tackled.
CHEESE
That's nice. Hey, as long as you're here, maybe you could tell us if you've ever been to the Almost Fresh Grocery Store or the Suds & Spuds?
Never to the Suds & Spuds, but I always go to the grocery store for free watermelon samples. So juicy. So delicious.
GRRR!

As he leaves, Chapster makes one last kind and incredibly spooky offer. . . .

Once the little creep...er, uh, tyke is gone, Logan gets an idea. She pulls a novel called *Sherlock Holmes and the Crumpet Thief* from her huge mystery library.

In the book, Sherlock Holmes sets a trap for the suspect on page seventy-two. He puts out a plate of crumpets and waits.
I get it! We can do the same thing with some spuds!
SHERLOCK HOLMES AND THE CRUMPET THIEF
SWIG
But I thought you had given me the boot?
You're on probation. If you haven't tackled any more kindergartners by the end of this case, you're back on the force.
Deal!

Murkee PRIDE
IN CASE A FIRST GRADER ATTACKS
MAKE SURE YOU'RE EQUIPPED
PROTECTIVE HELMET
NYLON NET
RUBBER BALLOTS
STEEL BOOTS
SAFETY FIRST!
HALL PASS
MISS MACKY
TODAY'S LUNCH SPECIAL
STEAK FLORENTINE WITH BABY SNAP PEAS
SIGN-IN SHEET

CHAPTER 5

OPERATION SMACKDOWN

The next morning, the Murkee Elementary office is hustling and bustling with the usual bunch of teachers, office ladies, and barfy kids looking to see the school nurse.

We've got to get to that intercom and make our fake announcement.

It'll take a miracle to get past Miss Macky.

Miss Macky, an office lady, guards the intercom microphone with a yardstick. Only she can make announcements without approval from Principal Shrub or, if he's unavailable, the president of the United States.

Office lady yardstick fighting stances

Fortunately, Logan has the perfect plan and Gustavo has the perfect mustache for getting the job done.

While Miss Macky shows Gustavo to the copy room, Logan darts for the intercom and puts on her best old-lady voice. . . .

Today's shipment of delicious potatoes will be kept in the janitor's closet under tight security until lunch period. Thank you!
STRYK FORCE
Someone's listening!
SENOR TADPOLES
A+
SURE DADDY

Hold up!! Who's that making announcements on my intercom?
You must be imagining things, lady. Perhaps you should consider retirement.
COPY
CLONE
TONER
BLUE INK
RED INK
BLACK INK
GOAT'S MILK
What's wrong with this copier?

It doesn't take long for Miss Macky to figure out she's been duped.

Luckily, Logan and Gustavo give her the slip without suffering the sting of the yardstick.

Where are Gustavo and Logan?
BOWLING SUPPLIES
WHIFF FOR SUDDEN ODORS
DRIED CRICKETS
COCOA-FLAVORED
BUBB
RE-MOVE
SCRUBBING CHAMP!
HEY, BUB!
SOAP
LAVA FLOW
CARPET DUST
LAUNDRY KING
POWDER IN A BOX!
SMELLS WEIRD
SPONGES
CHORE DETERGENT
AJAX
MIGHTY WASH
POLISH
SUDS DETERGENT
POISON
SCRUB N SCRUB
HAND SANITIZER
BULK TP
FOR BIG JOBS
EAR LOBE SANITIZER
POTATOES
Potato sack (Actually, it's filled with old socks and dirt clods.)

CHAPTER 6

A CLEAN FIGHT

Five minutes later. The janitor's closet. A lone bag of spuds sits on an overturned mop bucket. Logan and Gustavo wait in the shadows for the potato thief to take the bait. . . .

Nothing seems to be happening. Are you two sure this plan is going to work?

Suddenly, the little nightmare ninja gives Gustavo a swift kick in the chops!

Then he swoops in for the spuds, but Logan lays down a slick pool of pink bathroom soap!

Logan ties up the little rascal and Gustavo tears off the ninja suit to reveal . . .

It's crazy! The broom closet is full of Chapsters!

Suddenly, a Chapster swoops in with a blinding window-cleaner face-spray attack while another Chapster smacks Logan with a broom!

Then, a different Chapster unleashes the electric floor waxer on Gustavo!

Logan delivers a blistering karate chop, and her hand slices right through Chapster's fingers, sending tiny, crisp fingerling potatoes into the air!

The Chap attack is unrelenting! But Gustavo seems unfazed.

Finally, the Chapsters all escape through the air vent with the taters!

Logan and Gustavo run out of the broom closet and burst into Miss Perkle's kindergarten class next door!

But Chapster's been right here for the last hour, painting wonderful pictures for the class.
I just completed my portrait of Pinocchio doing the robot in a pepperoni factory. It is exquisite.
ART FOR TYKES
I ♥ CHEESE
Look closely!
SUSPECT
PUPPY LOVES BATH TIME!
ZOMBIE LOVES LUNCH TIME!

Moments later, in the principal's office yet again, Shrub has a few words to yell about Logan and Gustavo's behavior. . . .

Shrub gives them five more detentions and sends them on their way.

DO NOT DISTURB!
POTATOES
COMING SOON
VIC'S CEMETERY!
"LIE DOWN IN LUXURY!"
SPACE AVAILABLE!
Look for suspicious activity!

CHAPTER 7

BRINGING HOME THE BEACON

After school, the Snoop Troop combs the neighborhood, waiting for Gustavo's homing beacon to beep when they get close to the potato sack.

All of a sudden, Gustavo's mustache goes off like an alarm clock gone haywire!

The bushy beacon has led them to a crumbling, rusty, old garden shed. It looks about as inviting as a rattlesnake cupcake party.

Inside, it's dusty and junky and smells like sawdust.

There are books strewn about everywhere. And we're not talkin' just any ol' books—these are books about potatoes!

On the ground sits the sack full of socks and dirt. The little mini-mustache beacon is beeping away.

See if you can uncover the secret message in this pictogram!

The solution is obvious, but I'll let you go ahead and tell us what it is.
It says, "Army of Chapsters to steal gold at five PM on Friday!"
+Y
ARM+Y
-F
OF-F
+S
CHAPSTER+S
2
TO
ST+
ST+EEL
+D
GOAL+D
-C
CAT-C
PM
5:00 PM
ON
+
FRY+DAY!

Suddenly, they catch a whiff of something cooking, accompanied by strange munching and crunching sounds.

On the other side of the door sit a whole table of Chapsters! They are smacking and chomping and using their greasy little hands to stuff their mouths full of potatoes!

As they munch on the potato products, a TV in the corner features a live report from Dr. Snote about the toe-shaped potato. A shadowy figure emerges from behind some crates! That's when all the Chapsters suddenly notice Logan and Gustavo!

The Chapsters have spotted you. I suggest you guys get the heck out of there!

Gustavo trips on a rock on the way out and grabs on to a tarp. . . .

Behind the tarp is a giant tank with a Chapster suspended in it. From his shoulder sprouts a tiny disgusting mini-Chapster!!!

PO-PO
DO NOT DISTURB!
PO-PO

CHAPTER 8

HEY, BUD!

Within twenty minutes, Logan and Gustavo have called the cops and the shed is surrounded by Captain Mosely and his men.

Mosely decides to force his way in!

The shed is completely spotless! There's no sign of any water tanks, mutant Chapsters, or Tater Tots!
Tarps are neatly folded
Dust-free shelves
Welcoming environment
Shiny, polished tools
WELCOME
Complimentary breath mints
This might be the nicest shed I've ever seen. I'm considering moving in.
Rat in black tie

Someone must have covered up his or her tracks. The shed is clean, and Captain Mosely seems none too pleased to have been called out on his night off.

Back at the ice-cream truck, Logan and Gustavo dine on Fudgysickles and review what they've learned so far. . . .

Logan points at a scientific potato book she checked out from the Murkee Elementary library.

Logan starts doodling on her dry-erase board. Soon she arrives at her theory, and it's a doozy. . . .

Logan also concludes that the shady figure they saw hiding in the shadows in the shed is the same person who cloned Chapster.

I think we get your point! So, let me get this straight: The suspect is someone who has access to Chapster's DNA?

Logan lays out a map and searches for the most likely location for a gold robbery.

It doesn't take long to pinpoint the locale.

So, according to our map, the gold supply at Fort Bling-Bling could be the robbers' target in just an hour and a half. We need to interview all our suspects.
This calls for my NosePix 500 hidden-camera mustache. I'll be snapping important secret photos for our investigation.

CHAPTER 9

THE UNUSUAL SUSPECTS

It's the next day. Friday. 3:30 PM. As soon as school lets out, Logan and Gustavo rush over to the Almost Fresh Grocery Store. All is normal. Patrons are shopping. Sales are brisk. Diapers are half off.

Hey, Mr. Mister! Remember us? We were wondering if we could ask you something to help our investigation?
Why, of course! The junior detectives. I was just writing today's specials on our chalkboard.
DAILY S
We'll be quick. All we wanted to know is if you saw any of these folks in your store around the same time as the potato robbery?
CHAPSTER
CHAPSTER'S MOM
DR. SNOTE

Well, I've seen all of them in here at one time or another, but mostly little Chapster. He just loves slurpin' and slobberin' on our free watermelon samples. I always try to have a fresh batch out for him!
FREE SAMPLES
PLEASE SPIT SEEDS IN WASTE BASKET!
DIET
PRIMO
SLOP
DAILY SPECIALS
FRESH TOMATOES $2.99 lb.
BACON $3.29 lb.
EAR OF CORN 75¢
EAR OF SWINE 95¢
DANGER! SLIPPERY PORK CHOP!
Look closely!
SUSPECT

Well, that was disappointing. It didn't help narrow down our suspect list at all. Everyone goes to that grocery store.
Hey, anyplace where I can buy a fifty-ounce bag of extra-large marshmallows can't be all bad.
PUFF

Let's hope Dr. Snote is more helpful.
SHOTS R US
A PEDIATRICIAN WONDERLAND
SPECIAL! GIVE US A BREAK AND WE'LL GIVE YOU A BREAK! CASTS HALF-PRICE!
OPEN
DANGER SLIPPERY

In the examining room, Logan and Gustavo ask Dr. Snote whether or not he's ever gotten a DNA sample from Chapster.

There's not much more the doc can tell them, so they bid him farewell.

And question suspects they will. Next stop on the list—the lair of Chapster!

Okay, if there's one place less inviting than that shed full of clones or Dr. Snote's office, it's Chapster's house. Even a ghost might think twice before visiting this joint!

Inside, Chapster and his mom are busy drawing portraits of one of their prized stray cats.

After Logan politely refuses the fungi refreshments, she asks Chapster and his mom what they know about DNA, clones, and growing potatoes.

Hmm...interesting. She might not know about DNA, but she is into ninja martial arts and has plenty of experience growing bizarre food items in the house.
All I know is that, based on those cat portraits, both of them are terrible drawers.
Gustavo, you just might be onto something! Quick! Print out all the photos you've been taking!
This calls for more facial hair!
TERRIBLE DRAWERS
TERRIBLE DRAWERS
TERRIBLE DRAWERS
TERRIBLE DRAWERS

Gustavo slaps on his NosePix 500 printer-beard accessory and prints out all the photos he took of the suspects.

Logan examines the photos.

Wheelie examines his butt.

With only thirty minutes to go before the great gold robbery, Logan makes a special announcement.

STOP!

An Important Message from the Narrator

Hey, all you super sleuths! Here's your last chance to figure out who cloned Chapster before the Snoop Troop reveals it in the next chapter. If you can't figure it out, go back and look at each page with a magnifying glass labeled "Suspect" or "Clue," like the ones right here. Come on—impress me!

Which one of these shady characters clones kids, swipes spuds, and is gunnin' for gold?

CHAPSTER'S MOM? She likes martial arts and sure could use the money from a gold robbery for a home makeover.

MR. MISTER? He knows his taters.

DR. SNOTE? He's a smart doc with access to DNA.

CHAPSTER? Maybe he cloned himself. He likes to grow weird things in dark places.

Turn the page to find out who's a slimeball super villain!

I ♥ CHEESE
BUILD YOUR OWN CHEESE KIT
JUST ADD CURDLED MILK!
BUILD YOUR OWN CHEESE KIT

CHAPTER 10

WHO LET THE SPUDS OUT?

Logan and Gustavo gather everyone in the living room to reveal the perpetrator's identity.

At first, we thought maybe one of you did it. You both have access to Chapster's DNA, and you're always growing weird stuff, so why not half kid/half potatoes?
There is nothing weird about cheese and fungi, dear woman.
DNA
I ♥ CHEESE
Don't worry! We know neither of you could've drawn that pictogram we found. Judging from your cat portraits, you two are terrible artists! You couldn't draw flies on garbage day!
He's one to talk.

Our next suspect was Dr. Snote. He has the medical knowledge, access to the DNA in Chapster's blood sample, and a love for causing great pain.
DOC SNOTE
DNA
BLOOD
But when we saw the shadowy suspect in the shed, there was a live news report featuring Dr. Snote on TV. He was in front of reporters at the same time.
LIVE!

So, if Chapster and his mom and Dr. Snote are all innocent, who does that leave?

Suddenly, Mr. Mister bursts in with his posse of Chapster clones!

The clones tie everyone up in the living room. Logan asks Mr. Mister why on Earth he chose Chapster to model his army of robbing replicants after.

My Chapster clones are composed of potatoes, feed on potatoes, and reproduce like potatoes. I experimented with several different fruits and veggies at first.
The Bananachapster just did not work out at all. Very mushy and un-a-peeling!
Blarb! Blug!
Now I'm off to steal some gold! Don't even think about trying to wriggle free or call the cops, or the real Chapster gets it!
You brute!
I ♥ CHEESE

After Mr. Mister leaves, Logan and Gustavo try to squirm free of the ropes. Unfortunately, they're so tight, even Wheelie can't gnaw on them.

Orion!
Nexus!
Andromeda!
Commence claw maneuver!
CLAW!
SCRATCH!
Uh...okay, then. Let's call the cops and head to Fort Bling-Bling.
Good kitty.

FORT
BLING-BLING
MILLIONS IN GOLD INSIDE.
PLEASE LOCK DOOR BEFORE ← LEAVING.

CHAPTER 11

THE BIG CHAPSTACULAR!

Fort Bling Bling. 5:00 PM. It's quiet. Too quiet. Logan and Gustavo and Wheelie arrive on the scene ready to bust Mr. Mister and his Chapster crew.

Logan tries to warn the head of security, but he's not having it.

Suddenly, the security forces are surrounded by Chapsters!

The little tykes of terror swarm the officers like ants on a picnic basket!

The clones have infiltrated the building! Everything gold is in danger!

Logan and Gustavo are overtaken by the pernicious pipsqueaks.

How are we supposed to tell the real Chapster from the phonies?
If you'd been paying attention, you would have noticed that the real Chapster's T-shirt says, "I Love Cheese" while the clones' shirts say, "I Love Chess."
I ♥ CHESS
CHEESE
DANGER
CONSTRUCTION AREA

Find the real Chapster!
I ♥ CHESS

Gustavo finally spots him.

How in the heck are you guys going to get him down?

Gustavo's Grappling Stache V-7 launches a hook that latches on to the basket. Logan slowly shimmies up the rope attached to it.

She makes her way into the basket and boots out any unwanted passengers.

Scanning the horizon, Logan looks for any spot from which Mr. Mister could be controlling his army of spuds.

Look! He's in that produce truck! He must be sending out radio waves to the chips in the clones' noggins!
PRODUCE
Gustavo! You have to destroy the dish on top of that truck!
Consider it toast, 'cause I'm on it like margarine, *mamacita*!

Suddenly, the Chapster clones start jamming together into a huge mega clone clump that keeps getting bigger and bigger!

The clones have formed into a behemoth Chapsterzilla!

Logan, it looks like you're gonna have to stop Mr. Mister! Gustavo's too busy trying not to get stomped into mulch!

They start swinging the basket to and fro until the contraption can't possibly swing any higher!

At the highest point of the swing, Logan disconnects the basket, and they go hurtling through the air like a rocket!

The grocer's truck is flattened. His satellite dish destroyed!

Unfortunately, even with the satellite dish destroyed, the mega Chapster is still going strong, packing up all the loot and laying waste to the city!

Gustavo's words suddenly awaken something in Logan, and for once it's not anger.

The humongous Chapster freezes in place at the last second!

Finally, the air is filled with the sounds of sirens and screeching tires as Captain Mosely pulls up with his men.

BRAIN FREEZE
ICE CREAM
detectives for hire
ROCKET POP!
MYSTERY

CHAPTER 12

BACK ON THE FORCE

Days later, the Snoop Troop decides to take it easy. Chillin' and relaxin' are all that are on the agenda.

After all, it's exhausting being heroes. For saving the city, they had been awarded the Golden Scalloped Potato medallion. . . .

The clones had their mind-controlling potato chips snipped, and formed the world's biggest boy band. They are known for their killer mash-ups.

And Wheelie finally returned the remote control. . . . Please don't ask how.

But Logan and Gustavo's day of relaxation is interrupted by an unexpected guest. . . .

What are you doing here, kid?
I bring a gift of gratitude.
It's not more homegrown fungus, is it?
CHEESE

Negative. It is a heavy-duty drill master mustache with six interchangeable drill bits and screwdriver attachments.
I made it myself out of scrap metal and old kitty hairballs.

You have a talent, kid. We could use someone like you on the force, provided you stay in your house until we call you. You're kinda creepy.
CHEESE

Oh, and by the way, Gustavo: Probation is over. You're back on the Snoop Troop, rookie. Here's your magnifying glass. Try not to play Ping-Pong with it.
Oh, happy day!
I ♥ CHEESE

Our private eyes cherish the remainder of this peaceful day because they know it will not last.

There is already a foul wind and strange smell in the air. . . . Trouble is on the way!

DOODLE SNOOPS

Shoop Troop Case File #2

CLASSIFIED

Warning:
The following secret files may require doodling, scribbling, heavy thinking, and, possibly, yodeling!

Attention, shoppers!

CEREAL
ICE CREAM SPRINKLES
ICE CREAM SPRINKLES
ICE CREAM SPRINKLES
ICE CREAM SPRINKLES
BIG BOWL O' CARROTS
HONEY
YUK YUMS
FRUIT LOGS
LOOPZ
GATOR GLOPS
EXTRA SUGAR!
WITH NO ESSENTIAL VITAMINS!
SUGAR SPIKES
SUGAR RUSH
HEY O'S
FIRE ANTS!
See if you can spot all of the dangers to the Almost Fresh shoppers!

Captain Mosely needs your help!

CHAPSTER WANNA CRACKER?
EIGHT-ARMED CHAPSTERPUS
DANGER!!! ELECTRIC CHAPSTER REPTILIAN INSIDE!

HOW TO DRAW CHAPSTER

1. Start with his stylish hairdo, like half a grapefruit turned over.

2. Add his beady little eyes, like two black-eyed peas.

3. Don't forget a sniffer and his two front teeth.

4. Check out the set of ears on this kid!

5. How about some stubby little arms? Careful—those hands are coated in bologna grease!

6. Be sure to add his favorite T-shirt! Now you have a new best friend!

HOW TO DRAW A POTATO

1. First draw an oblong blob, like a football that's been left in the sun all summer.

2. Now add little bumps and eyes.

3. This tater's getting ripe, so let's add a little sprout coming out of it, like a stylish ponytail.

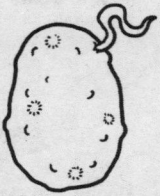

4. Slap some leaves on there!

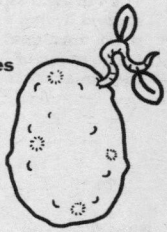

5. Now add some more eyes. We're talking real eyes this time, with luscious lashes!

6. Add some teeth and a swanky sweater. Congratulations! Your date for the Murkee Elementary Dance has arrived!

HOW TO DRAW A NINJA

1. The eyes come first, angry and round, like enraged kumquats.

2. Next is the nose, like a lounging lima bean.

3. Then draw a square around it, like a party envelope. This is the mask of the ninja.

4. The shape of the head must match he who wears the mask.

5. Now, draw the body, preferably in a martial arts battle stance!

6. Finally, add classic ninja weaponry, like the throwing star and salami nunchacku!

HOW TO DRAW CAPTAIN MOSELY

1. Draw the eyes with furry-caterpillar brows above them.

2. Now, a big ol' schnozz with an impressive mustache, like two big, fuzzy tarantula legs.

3. Time for the square jaw and round ears.

4. Follow that with a big, round head of hair, like a poodle that's just stepped out of a dryer.

5. Make sure you draw his body in a stance that says, "Don't mess with me, kid!"

6. Finally, give him a tie and don't forget the sassy one-liner.

CRACKPOT

A security cam snapped two pics of the Snoop Troop in action, but something doesn't look right about that second photo.

SNAPSHOT

Pick out the differences before it gets plastered all over the news. Answers are on the next page. No cheating, or Chapster will force you to eat his homemade cheese-curd porridge!

HAIR WE GO AGAIN!
I AM THE WALRUS.
HAVING A BALL
BURSTING OUT ALL OVER
MAY CONTAIN NUTS
CAT HAIR
NUTTY BEHAVIOR
I ♡ CHEESE
POP GOES THE WEASEL!
EMOTICON JOB
IN THE BAG
DYNO-MITE!
GOOFIN' OFF
MOLD
CASH MONEY
MOLDY BUT A GOODIE
BUGGIN' OUT
FLASHING SOME GREEN

Help! Mr. Mister, the mean green grocer, has sent another pictogram! See if you can figure it out before that scoundrel strikes again!

(answers on next page)

Answer:
I want 100 bowls of ice cream by tonight or else!

Sketch the magnified clue!

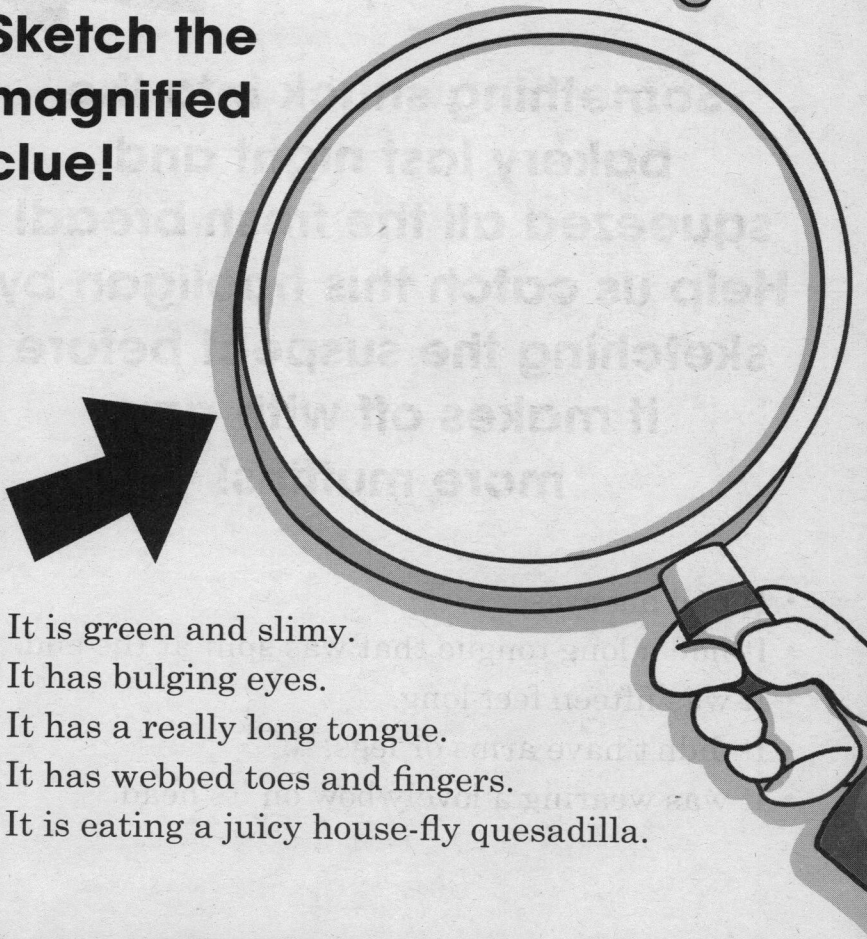

- It is green and slimy.
- It has bulging eyes.
- It has a really long tongue.
- It has webbed toes and fingers.
- It is eating a juicy house-fly quesadilla.

Something snuck into the bakery last night and squeezed all the fresh bread! Help us catch this hooligan by sketching the suspect before it makes off with any more muffins!

- It had big eyes.
- It had a long tongue that was split at the end.
- It was fifteen feet long.
- It didn't have arms or legs.
- It was wearing a lovely bow on its head.

MUSTACHE ART
CREATE YOUR OWN HI-TECH COOKIE DUSTER!

WORD SEARCH

Z	G	M	I	C	R	O	S	C	O	P	E	I	O	A	C	K
C	O	J	C	A	T	S	V	H	H	N	I	N	J	A	S	I
H	U	X	O	L	H	M	C	A	T	K	T	A	I	L	W	D
I	D	S	O	B	P	N	F	I	E	C	R	O	U	C	I	S
P	A	R	M	E	S	A	N	R	S	H	A	K	D	H	S	C
K	I	T	T	Y	P	E	T	B	T	E	P	F	C	C	S	L
Q	U	E	S	O	S	L	A	A	T	D	A	T	A	R	X	O
S	T	I	N	K	Y	S	D	L	U	D	H	R	P	F	E	N
C	A	T	N	I	P	W	B	L	B	A	F	J	S	T	S	E
D	N	A	Q	O	F	O	L	A	E	R	D	T	W	I	N	S

Look for words involving the three C's: Cats, Clones, and Cheese!

DOODLE SNOOPS ANSWER KEY

WORD SEARCH:

Z	G	M	I	C	R	O	S	C	O	P	E	I	O	A	C	K
C	O	J	C	A	T	S	V	H	H	N	I	N	J	A	S	I
H	U	X	O	L	H	M	C	A	T	K	T	A	I	L	W	D
I	D	S	O	B	P	N	F	I	E	C	R	O	U	C	I	S
P	A	R	M	E	S	A	N	R	S	H	A	K	D	H	S	C
K	I	T	T	Y	P	E	T	B	T	E	P	F	C	C	S	L
Q	U	E	S	O	S	L	A	A	T	D	A	T	A	R	X	O
S	T	I	N	K	Y	S	D	L	U	D	H	R	P	F	E	N
C	A	T	N	I	P	W	B	L	B	A	F	J	S	T	S	E
D	N	A	Q	O	F	O	L	A	E	R	D	T	W	I	N	S

KIRK SCROGGS

is the author and illustrator of *Snoop Troop: It Came from Beneath the Playground*, as well as the Tales of a Sixth-Grade Muppet series and the Wiley & Grampa's Creature Features series. He lives in Los Angeles.